The Red Kit and the Green Kite

written by Jay Dale

illustrated by Sharon Harmer

Dad and Jill
went to the park.

3

"Here is a green kite
for you," said Dad.
"And here is my red kite."

"I like my green kite,"
said Jill.
"It is going up, up, up."

"I like my red kite,"
said Dad.
"It is going up, up, up, too."

"Oh, no!" cried Jill.
"My green kite
is in the water."

"Oh, no!" said Dad.
"My red kite is going
in the water, too!"

"Come on," said Dad.
"Here is your green kite.
And here is my red kite."

"Look!" said Jill.
"My green kite
is **not** coming down.
And your red kite
is **not** coming down.
They are going up."

The green kite
and the red kite
went up, up, up.